Strange Curses

Bernhardt J. Hurwood

SCHOLASTIC BOOK SERVICES
NEW YORK • TORONTO • LONDON • AUCKLAND • SYDNEY • TOKYO

Copyright © 1975 by Bernhardt J. Hurwood.
All rights reserved. Published by
Scholastic Book Services, a division of
Scholastic Magazines, Inc.

1st printing March 1975
Printed in the U.S.A.

Table of Contents

The Subject of Curses
and a Few Famous Ones 4
The Curse of the Lambtons 15
The Rudesheim Curse 26
The Coruisk Horror 41
The Curse of the Shepherd 58
The Curse of the Gypsy 72
The Curse of Moy 83
The Curse of the Mummy's Foot . 95
Curses That Backfire 107

The Subject of Curses and a Few Famous Ones

We don't think very much about curses or cursing any more. The whole custom has pretty well gone out of style. These days if someone deliberately wrongs you, you either react within the framework of the law, or you take pains to avoid the person altogether. The last thing any sensible individual thinks of when provoked nowadays is to put a curse on anyone, because there are too many more practical alternatives. Yet at one time, the invocation of a curse was about as commonplace as a lawsuit is today. Like lawsuits, however, curses were not always effective. Yet because they were so common we still have a few hangovers from the past. For example, in times gone by, when people said, "God damn you!" they meant exactly that. They were calling upon God to condemn the soul of the person at whom their curse was aimed to everlasting damnation in the fires of hell. That was serious business, and to call upon heaven to take such drastic action required careful consideration. Consequently, even though we don't take such curses literally any more, there are many people who still take a dim view of the words "damn" and "hell," because of what they once represented. In fact, the use of these words is still regarded by many as "cursing."

But the kind of curses we're interested in here are much more complicated than casual one-line expletives. They involve dark deeds, heinous crimes, jealousies, hatreds, star-crossed lovers, fantastic occurrences, and chilling accounts of vengeance from beyond the grave. There are even tales involving weird, horrifying monsters.

Generally speaking, the more complicated the curse, the more devastating and far-reaching its results. Some are grim beyond measure, such as the legend of Germany's infamous Mouse Tower and the medieval curse that supposedly destroyed its builder, Bishop Hatto of Mayence.* Many

* *Haunted Houses,* Scholastic 1972.

curses about which we read involve houses and castles doomed to perpetual hauntings as the result of dreadful incidents, others are sagas of horror in which entire families are wiped out or forced to suffer generations of affliction merely because of an ancestor's misdeed. There are even stories in which the unfortunate victims of curses are doomed to become vampires.

Curses have been the central theme of countless stories of mystery and intrigue, and some of the most celebrated works of literature and music fall into this fascinating, spine-chilling class of fiction. What listener to the melancholy legend of the Flying Dutchman has not shivered at least once while hearing the tale? One of Richard Wagner's most famous operas is based upon the legend. As the story goes, there is a ghostly ship with blood-red sails that is doomed to ply the seven seas forever. According to sailors, to see this spectral vessel is an evil omen. The story is that its captain, centuries ago, while fighting heavy seas on a voyage around South Africa, swore a blasphemous oath that he would sail around the Cape of Good Hope if it took him forever. As punishment he and his crew were doomed to their terrible voyage, which would end only if the captain were to find a wife who was willing to sacrifice everything for him.

Perhaps the most tragic and dreadful curse ever to be recorded is the ancient Greek legend of the doom that fell on the house of Laius. This was immortalized by the Greek dramatist Sophocles in his plays, *Oedipus Tyrannos, Oedipus at Colonus,* and *Antigone.* There are many versions of the legend but essentially the story is this: Laius, king of Thebes, having committed a loathsome act of rape, was doomed by the gods not only to personal punishment, but to have tragedy, suffering, and punishment passed on to all his descendants. When he married Jocasta, the Delphic oracle warned Laius that he would be killed by his son. To thwart the prophecy, Laius, when a son was born, had a spike thrust through the infant's feet and abandoned him on Mount Cithaeron where he would be devoured by wild beasts. But the Fates had another destiny in store for the child: He was rescued by a shepherd and taken to the king of Corinth, who was childless. He decided to raise the orphan as his own son, naming him Oedipus, which means "swollen foot."

When he grew up Oedipus visited the Delphic oracle, who warned him that he would kill his father and marry his own mother. In order to prevent this from happening, he decided not to return to Corinth. On the road he encountered a chariot, driven by an arrogant man who ordered him off to one side so that his chariot might pass. Harsh words led to blows. In the end Oedipus killed the charioteer and four of his five attendants. The man he killed was Laius, king of Thebes, his real father. So was the oracle's prophecy fulfilled and the grounds laid for later tragedy.

Laius had been on his way to Delphi to consult the oracle about a horrible plague attacking Thebes. The Sphinx, a dreadful monster with the head of a woman, the body of a lion, and the wings of an eagle, was ravaging the city. She had been sent by the goddess Hera to punish the city for Laius' crimes. She perched outside the city asking every traveler a riddle: "What creature has only one voice but walks sometimes on two feet, sometimes on three, sometimes on four, and is weakest when it walks on the most?" Whoever failed to answer the riddle was torn to bits and devoured. None had succeeded in answering all but many had failed. Thebes trembled in terror.

As Oedipus approached the city and was challenged by the Sphinx, he answered, "Man. He crawls on four feet as an infant, walks on two in his prime, and leans upon a staff in old age." Upon hearing this the mortified Sphinx dashed herself to pieces in the valley below. Oedipus was given a hero's welcome, and Creon, the regent, ruling temporarily after Laius' death, offered Oedipus the crown as a reward for having freed Thebes from the Sphinx. As was customary, Oedipus was also offered the hand of the queen in marriage. He could not know she was his own mother.

For a number of years Oedipus ruled in peace, but then a famine descended upon the city. Once again he journeyed to Delphi to consult the oracle, who declared, "Expel the murderer of Laius and the famine will be lifted." Totally unaware that the murderer was none other than himself, Oedipus pronounced a curse on that unknown assassin and decreed that he be exiled when captured. Next, having no idea where to begin his search, Oedipus consulted Tiresias, a blind soothsayer, who revealed not only that the reigning king was the murderer of Laius, but that he had married his own mother, Jocasta, and fathered two sons and two daughters by her.

Driven mad by shame and guilt, Jocasta hanged herself. Oedipus, overcome by the same powerful emotions, seized the golden buckles of her dress and put out his own eyes, declaring that they were unworthy ever again to see the golden light of day. Shunned even by his sons, Eteocles and Polyneices, Oedipus cursed them and went into exile. For many years he wandered from country to country with his faithful daughter Antigone until she led him at last to the grove of the Furies at Colonus in Attica. He did not fear them, however, for he did not believe himself capable of any further suffering.

Yet, Oedipus had to endure a final ordeal. All he wanted was to remain in the grove and die peacefully under the protection of Theseus, king of Athens. Now, however, the Thebans wanted him back. The oracle at Delphi had warned that Thebes was doomed to dreadful tragedy if the body of Oedipus was not buried there. Intrigue was heaped upon intrigue in the struggle to force Oedipus to return: His daughters were kidnapped by Creon, but later rescued by the king of Athens. Next, his faithless son Polyneices came and tried to enlist his support in a fratricidal war. Oedipus, recognizing the young man's selfish motives, declared, "Dry were your eyes, hard as stone your heart, dumb your lips, when I went from Thebes friendless and alone. Here then is your reward: Before the walls of Thebes you shall perish, pierced by your brother's hand, and there your brother shall die, slain by you."

Oedipus finally died and was buried in a secret tomb. But the curse that rested so heavily on his family remained. Just as he had said, Polyneices and Eteocles died, each at the hand of the other. Creon, still ruler of Thebes, angered at the dead Polyneices for having attempted to conquer the city, decreed that his body be left unburied. Antigone, in defiance of the order crept out under cover of darkness to give her brother a decent burial. She was caught and walled up alive in a cave. Upon hearing this, Tiresias warned Creon that his harsh decree had angered the gods, and that if he did not rescue Antigone at once, his own son Haemon would die. Unfortunately, Creon arrived at the cave too late. Antigone had hanged herself. Haemon, overcome with rage and grief, spat upon his father and committed suicide on the spot. When Creon's wife heard of this, she too took her own life. Upon learning what had happened, Creon could go on no longer. He had himself banished and went into exile, the final victim of an epic tragedy.

Not every account of a curse contains such details of devastating horrors. There are occasional instances of curses that either wear themselves out or manage one way or another to get undone. An intriguing example of the latter comes also from Greece but not from ancient times. Before telling the story, though, it would be wise to offer an explanation about some of its details.

For centuries Greek peasants have believed that anyone who becomes the victim of a certain type of curse is doomed to become a vampire after death, or, at very least, his body will not decay and the possibility of his becoming a vampire remains strong. Typical of such curses are, "May the earth not receive thee," or "May the black earth spew thee up," or "Mayest thou become in the grave like rigid wood."

Naturally, anyone who believed in such curses was very anxious to avoid one if at all possible, especially if during the course of a lifetime these words were ever uttered in haste and then forgotten. There were many problems, because curses imposed by certain persons were regarded as more effective than others. The most potent curses were those that came from the lips of parents, godfathers, and members of the clergy. In fact, a godfather's curse was regarded as stronger even than that of a bishop. Now, since it was quite possible for a person to go through life having cursed a large number of people and not be able to remember the exact details of every curse, it was regarded as good form when on the verge of death to perform a ceremony with the aid of a priest which would dissolve all the curses. It was a simple ritual. The dying person would drop some salt in water and solemnly declare, "As this salt dissolves, so may all my curses." This was very important because it was necessary for the person who had originally invoked the curse to remove it. The following story illustrates how strong such a curse can be, even after a series of unexpected circumstances:

Many, many years ago a certain archbishop of Salonica cursed a man by exclaiming, "May the earth not receive thee!" As time passed the archbishop forgot about the matter and in the course of his travels decided to leave the church and become a Moslem. He was a man of such wisdom and learning that in time he became a mullah, or teacher of Mohammedan law and dogma.

Meanwhile, the man he had cursed died and was buried. For some reason or other the tomb was opened three years afterwards and to everyone's horror the body was as fresh as it had been on the day it was put in the coffin. Candles were burned and prayers were offered, but nothing happened to the body and everyone was distraught. In despair they sealed the corpse back in its tomb. Three years later the body was examined again. Still it looked as though it had been freshly buried; the flesh had not turned to dust. The unhappy widow's consternation was great and then she recalled that her deceased husband had once been the victim of a malediction from the ex-archbishop.

She went to see him at once and tearfully

13

begged him to undo the curse he had uttered so many years before. Understanding the poor woman's predicament he agreed to do what he could. Since he was no longer a Christian he had to obtain permission from the authorities to perform the necessary rite, but this proved to be no obstacle for they sympathized immediately with the woman's plight. As soon as the formalities were attended to the former churchman went to the tomb, had it opened, and gazed for a moment on the lifeless face of the corpse. Then he knelt down and began to pray, employing a litany of his former faith. Apparently his episcopal powers had not deserted him, for not a moment after he had finished and risen to his feet, the flesh of the corpse shriveled and crumbled to dust until there was nothing left but a clean white skeleton. With that the bones were reinterred and presumably everyone concerned returned to the normal pursuit of his business.

The Curse of
the Lambtons

The Lambtons were a rich and noble English family who lived in a castle dating back to about the twelfth century. They had a reputation of being proud and courageous, especially in battle. There was also a reckless quality to their behavior, and they were said to fear no man, no devil, nor even God. Despite these characteristics they were mostly decent people who were respected by almost all who knew them. They were certainly not extreme in their behavior, although occasionally one of them seemed to be the very model for the overall family reputation. Such a man was John Lambton, Knight of Rhodes, also the man who inadvertently set in motion the events that eventually resulted in a terrible family curse.

According to tradition, the bizarre chain of

circumstances leading up to the curse began on a bright summer Sunday morning when young John Lambton decided that instead of going to church with the rest of his family he would go fishing. Such an action in those days was regarded as a serious and blasphemous breach of conduct. Consequently, his presence, angling on the banks of the River Weir, scandalized all who saw him as they passed on their way to church. Apparently the fish were not biting well that day, and Lambton did not catch any. This made him angry. He began uttering a series of withering curses which were the early fifteenth century equivalent to X-rated language. It was considered bad enough to fish on a Sunday then, but to openly shout such blistering profanity was enough to make strong men cross themselves and turn pale.

Eventually he felt a powerful tug on his line and in triumph he began pulling it in, but when he finally got his catch out of the water he was appalled beyond belief. Instead of a fish, there dangled on his hook the most hideous looking reptilian creature he had ever seen in his life. Scaly and dripping with slime, it had baleful green eyes, sharp yellow teeth, and a stench like a thousand dung heaps. As he struggled to remove the revolting thing from his line, Lambton backed away from the river and by the time he had removed it he was alongside a well, down which he immediately flung the disgusting monster. Sighing with relief when it disappeared beneath the surface he did no more fishing that day and returned to the castle.

For some time afterwards John Lambton reflected on his experience that morning, and finally concluded that it was a warning of some sort to mend his ways. He felt that perhaps he had offended God once too often and it was now high time to do some serious penance. It so happened that at the time an alliance of Christian princes was fighting a war against the Turks in the East. One of the most highly regarded methods of saving one's soul was to take up the sword and slaughter the followers of Mohammed in the name of Christ.

Lambton remained at war for a full seven years. When he returned home he was told a fantastic story that filled his heart with dread. The repulsive creature he'd fished from the river that almost forgotten Sunday morning seven years past had not remained at the bottom of the well. It had grown into a ferocious, giant worm, slithered out of the well, and established itself on nearby Fatfield Hill. It had continued to grow until it was able to wrap itself around the hill three full times. There it remained most of the time, but when it grew hungry it ventured out to ravage the country-side until it had all but devoured every cow, sheep, and pig in the neighborhood. It had also preyed on a fair number of human victims as well, leaving the entire area in a state of consternation and terror.

A number of knights from all over England had come determined to slay the monster, but all had died in the attempt, falling instead as victims to its insatiable appetite. Naturally, upon hearing this tale of woe, John Lambton was overcome with guilt. After all, if he had not gone fishing that Sunday, he would never have caught the worm that had grown to such disastrous proportions. His sense of responsibility for this terrible state of affairs was heightened by the fact that the thing was generally referred to as "The Lambton Worm." It should be mentioned here, that if the word "worm" seems a bit odd when applied to something that more rightly appears to be a dragon, the oddness is purely a modern phenomenon. In old Anglo-Saxon times the word *wyrm* or *wurm* was used interchangeably to mean *serpent* or *dragon*.

In any case, John Lambton made up his mind that since he was responsible for this scourge, he either had to kill it or die trying. After having managed to survive seven years of bloody battle, however, he was no longer the reckless youth he had been before leaving to fight the Turks. He was willing to risk his life, but he had no intention of taking unnecessary chances. He recalled that there was an old woman living in the vicinity who was generally regarded to be a witch. Although she was not known to have done anything specific to harm anyone she was greatly feared, and the people of the county rarely had dealings with her unless it was a matter of life or death. Naturally, no one ever admitted to having had anything to do with her, but judging by the common knowledge of the services she performed, the good folk who did call upon her were most adept at keeping secrets. He decided to seek her out.

Determined not to waste any time, Lambton set out to find the wise woman the very day he learned what had come of his ill-fated morning of fishing. He knew approximately where she lived, somewhere in a wood not far from Lambton Castle. It was just about sundown when he left, and as the spreading red glow of the horizon gradually changed to purple, the shadows lengthened and grew darker. So deserted was the countryside that for an instant Lambton felt as though he were the only soul on earth venturing into a darkening world of tangled thickets, twisted branches, and polished, skull-like rocks. It was a place inhabited by creatures of the night, unseen things that hooted and croaked and flapped leathery wings, things that hissed and squeaked and slithered and moaned.

Shuddering as he made his way through the gathering darkness, Lambton thought of how much more he would have preferred the roar of battle to this strange uncanny quiet. Enemies brandishing swords, maces, and battle axes could be met face to face and fought. Here there was nothing but sound and shadow, mist and gloom. But despite his discomfort he kept pressing forward until at last he came to a clearing in the woods. A pale moon had risen, bathing the clearing in a cool eerie light. Just as he was beginning to wonder if he would ever find the woman he sought, he heard a crackling sound at the far end where the wood began again. Looking up through the murk he saw a figure approach. It was hooded and robed in black, and as he stood motionless, one hand poised over the hilt of his dagger, it drew nearer. His heart began beating wildly in his chest, but a moment later he relaxed, for beneath the hood was the face of an old woman, the woman he'd been seeking, the witch of the wood.

Before he could say a word she pointed a long bony finger at him and spoke. "So, John Lambton," she said, "you have finally come to seek my counsel."

20

"I have been away at the wars for seven years," he replied haughtily.

"Seven years of evil and tears thanks to the monstrous worm you unleashed in our midst."

"By God's wounds, madam!" he retorted, "I came not to hear accusations, but to seek counsel. Will you give it or will you not?"

"Aye," she snapped, "I will give you counsel, but mark well my words lest you bring sore affliction to the house of Lambton."

"I have come to wipe out affliction, not bring it."

"Very well," she replied. "Then listen carefully to what I advise, and follow my instructions to the letter."

"I am listening."

The old woman paused, then fixing Lambton with a piercing look, declared, "Before I speak you must swear me a solemn oath."

"What sort of oath?" he demanded.

"You must swear that after you have slain the worm you must kill the first living creature you see."

"And if I do not?"

"If you do not, if you violate your oath, for nine generations hence, no Lord of Lambton will die in his bed."

"I am an honorable man!" he declared.

21

"Then swear!"

"I do so solemnly swear to your conditions," he replied.

"So be it, John Lambton. Now I shall tell you how to slay the monster."

With that she instructed him to have a special suit of armor constructed, one that was studded all over with razor sharp blades of steel. "Protected within such a suit," she explained, "and wielding the weapons you know so well, you will vanquish the creature."

As he returned to the castle, Lambton pondered deeply over the old woman's words. To wear such a suit of armor was good common sense, but to have sworn an oath promising to kill the first living creature he encountered after destroying the worm troubled him. He anticipated no difficulty in fulfilling it — it would be no problem for him to arrange such a matter: nevertheless he felt uneasy.

Early the next morning John Lambton summoned his armorer and ordered a special suit of armor, insisting that it be made with the utmost haste. It was not something which could be made overnight, but after several weeks it was ready and Lambton was prepared to have his final confrontation with the worm. Before he left, however, he called his father and told him that when he was victorious he would blow a triple blast on his hunting horn. Upon hearing this signal the elder Lambton was to release one of his son's favorite hunting dogs. By killing the dog the oath he had made to the witch would be fulfilled.

Finally prepared, John Lambton buckled on his sword and made his way to Fatfield Hill, where the worm lay coiled and waiting. As he drew near, the monster raised its ugly head and stared balefully at him with its gleaming, plate-sized eyes. Then hissing malevolently, it uncoiled itself and began slithering toward him. With his sword in his right hand and a dagger in his left, Lambton advanced suddenly. Before he knew what had happened, the great serpent sprang and in an instant had wrapped itself around him. Under ordinary circumstances he would have been crushed to death, but because of the blades protruding from his armor, the worm was severely wounded and as it moved great chunks of its flesh were instantly sliced off. Unwrapping itself and backing off it hissed horribly. To Lambton's horror the hacked-off pieces were gathered up by the creature and reconnected to its body as if they had never been severed at all.

Again the worm darted forward, coiling itself around its human adversary, and again was forced to retreat because of the damage the blades in the armor inflicted. But it was only a matter of moments before the monster was whole again and moving in for another attack.

Matters progressed in this fashion for several hours and Lambton concluded that unless he changed his tactics the battle would wind up in a draw. Now, behind him was the river from which he had originally taken the monstrosity. Maintaining an aggressive stance he began slowly retreating toward the riverbank, but making certain first that he selected a spot where the water was not over his head, yet where the current was reasonably strong. He had swum and fished the river since early childhood and he knew its every turn and eddy.

As he stepped back into the river the worm no doubt thought that it had him trapped, for it lunged forward and seized him once again in its terrible coils. Down they went into the water, thrashing about in the churning stream in what had to be the death struggle for one of them. Again the razorlike blades protruding from Lambton's armor cut into the monster's flesh, slicing away huge chunks with its every move, but this time instead of rejoining the wounded monster's body, they were washed away by the current. Taking advantage of this the knight kept hacking with his sword until at last, with a final shudder and lashing of its bleeding tail, the loathsome creature finally expired.

Dragging himself wearily from the scene of his triumph and onto dry land, Lambton lifted his horn and blew the triple blast he had promised were he to be victorious. His father, overjoyed at the signal heralding the worm's destruction, forgot to release the hound, and went personally to the riverbank to congratulate his son. At the sight of his own father, John Lambton's heart sank, for he knew he had promised to kill the first living creature he met after slaying the worm. He had fully intended to keep his word, even if it meant the death of his favorite hound, but he could not harm his father and instead of striking with his sword, sheathed it instead.

According to the legend he did kill his dog afterward as a kind of substitute sacrifice, but it apparently did no good. The curse laid its icy hand on the shoulder of every Lord of Lambton for the next nine generations, each one of whom died either by violence or accident, the last of whom is believed to have been Henry, Lord Lambton, who died in his carriage while crossing a bridge in the year 1761.

The Rudesheim Curse

Rudesheim is a beautiful town on the River Rhine in the heart of one of the great German wine-growing regions. It is a very old town with a treasure chest of legends, one of the most intriguing centering around a brave but hard-headed knight, a pair of ill-fated lovers, and a curse that is said to linger in the region to this day.

The story began more than seven hundred years ago in a sweltering desert beyond Jerusalem. A small band of Prussian crusaders, broiling like lobsters in their leather and armor battle garb, were overtaken by a superior force of Saracens, and after a short but furious battle were defeated. Upon refusing the customary offer of freedom on

condition that they embrace the faith of Mohammed, they were placed in chains and marched on
foot to a distant fortress where they were to be
imprisoned indefinitely.

Their trek across the burning sands, dragging
their shackles as the sun beat mercilessly down
upon them, was torture enough, but their prison,
a hot, dark, and filthy dungeon crawling with
vermin, stank like a garbage heap. One of the
prisoners, Hans von Rudesheim, Lord of Rudesheim castle, sat brooding one day and cursing his
fate. As he crushed a scorpion beneath one foot
he raised his eyes toward the iron grating above
his cell to catch a glimpse of light. At that moment
he clasped his hands together and knelt down on
one knee. He made a solemn vow that if he ever
escaped from this prison he would dedicate his
daughter, Margaret, to the service of God by
putting her in a convent. Although the thought
probably never crossed his mind, he was doing
nothing more than promising to imprison his
daughter for life in return for his own, hardly a
loving gesture by any standards, nevertheless, a
common one in medieval times.

Meanwhile he passed the time matching wits
with rats, killing scorpions and other pests, and
feeding birds through the grating of his cell. One

27

day he noticed a pigeon among the other birds and on a wild impulse he ripped off a piece of his shirt, inscribed his name, the name of the fortress, and the word "help," using his own blood for ink. Carefully rolling the ragged piece of cloth up, he waited until another pigeon appeared some days later. As it was eating crumbs he seized its leg, fastened his message, and let the bird go. Von Rudesheim knew that the chances of his comrades ever seeing the message were slim, but he also knew that if he did not at least try, he would hate himself forever. After the bird had flown he reaffirmed his oath that if he were to escape from prison he would place his daughter in a religious order for the rest of her life.

What von Rudesheim did not know as he lay rotting in his pestilential dungeon was that a band of his fellow Prussian crusaders was encamped within a day's march. There one evening, as dusk was gathering, a pair of von Rudesheim's one-time companions, Kurt Lehndorf and Wilhelm Bosch, were watching the sunset and talking of other times. As they reminisced about their boyhood days they were joined by a third man, Rudolf Schramm. He was a strange and moody sort, given to long periods of silent meditation and he had the reputation of being a loner. Yet at times he was a thoroughly engaging companion, and his bravery outweighed his lack of social graces.

"Well, my friends," he called out. "How would you like to see into the future?"

"What are you talking about?" demanded Lehndorf, who looked upon such topics with great disfavor.

"Exactly what I said," repeated Schramm. "How would you like to know what the future has in store for you?"

"Our future is in the hands of the Almighty God," said Bosch. "What difference does it make whether we know it or not?"

"To me, it makes no difference at all," observed Schramm. I have seen my fate and I have accepted it. I thought you might care to do the same."

Lehndorf sneered. "Are you proposing to tell our fortunes, like some wandering beggar seeking alms?"

"Not at all," retorted Schramm. "Let me tell you what happened to me and judge for yourselves. You know that clump of rocks beyond our camp, the ones that lie between us and the hills? I was strolling about there by myself after our midday meal and the heat of the sun was so great I decided to find some shade. Well, luck was with me because I came upon a cave at the foot of the

29

hills and I ventured in to cool myself. It was black as the pit in there but my curiosity got the better of me and I continued to follow the passage for it was wide, and as my eyes grew accustomed to the darkness I had little difficulty in finding my way.

"It was so comfortable and cool, I sat down to rest myself and as I leaned back I thought I heard the drip of water off to my right. 'Aha!' I said to myself, 'there must be an underground stream nearby.' And right away I remembered that I was parching from thirst. I picked myself up and listened closely to determine exactly from whence I heard the sound and at that moment I saw a flicker of light just beyond where I stood. I pointed my nose in that direction and followed it, and before long I found myself in a huge chamber in the midst of which sat a hooded figure, cloaked in rags. Beside him was a small oil lamp that gave off a dim and smoky light. I was so astonished that I stopped in my tracks, and at that very moment he looked up and said to me, in perfect German, 'Greetings, Rudolf Schramm; welcome to my abode. Be seated and see what fate has destined for you.' "

"Surely you don't expect us to believe such a wild tale," scoffed Bosch.

"I can prove every word of it," retorted

Schramm. "Do me the courtesy of hearing me out first."

"We are listening," retorted Lehndorf, folding his arms across his chest and fixing Schramm with a cool stare.

"Well," Schramm continued, "you can imagine what went through my mind. I peered at the fellow, hardly believing my ears, not knowing what to do, when he said, 'Do not be afraid. I am Zadeek the hermit. Come sit beside me and discover your future.' A strange calm overcame me and I did as he told me. Scarcely had I seated myself when he reached beneath the folds of his robe and brought forth a mirror in a golden frame. 'Take this,' he said, 'and learn your fate.' I felt strangely light-headed as I took it from his hand. To my amazement I saw no reflection, only a vision of churning clouds. But then they cleared and I saw a terrible image as distinctly as I see the two of you now. A battle was raging and in its midst lay the figure of a dead crusader, an infidel lance buried in his chest. And as I looked more closely I recognized the face. It was my own!" Schramm sighed and forced a crooked smile. "Well," he said, "I suppose it is better to die in your prime than to grow old and feeble." He sighed again. "So there's my story. If you still don't believe me, go visit the cave yourselves. I

31

hope you have better futures than I." And with that he turned and walked away.

Although they were still skeptical, Lehndorf and Bosch were unable to resist the challenge. As soon as Schramm had left they agreed to go to the cave and see if there really was such a hermit there, for the temptation of seeing into the future was more than they could resist.

Before setting off to the cave the two crusaders procured a lantern and then they were off. With only the edge of the hills against the darkening sky to guide them they made their way to the cave and reached its mouth in less than an hour. Pausing only long enough to light their lantern they cautiously made their way inside and before long they found themselves in the presence of the hermit. Everything was as Schramm had described it to them. When the hooded figure of the old man raised its head their hearts began to pound. But they were dumbfounded when they heard themselves addressed by name and invited to come forward in order that they might learn their fates.

Lehndorf took the golden mirror first. It was just as he had been told it would be. First a cloudy turbulence, then a dissolving of the mist followed by an incredible series of moving images. There he was, in mortal combat with a fearsome Saracen. Noiselessly they struck blow after blow, thrusting, clubbing, and slashing each other with their weapons. Then without any warning, Lehndorf stumbled on a rock, losing his balance. That split second of an advantage was all his adversary needed. With a single well-aimed swing the Saracen struck. His gleaming blade swished through the air and neatly separated the hapless German from his head.

Stunned at the vivid preview of his final moments he wordlessly handed the mirror to his friend Bosch, who saw himself struggling to swim across the turbulent waters of a wide river. A look of sharp distress was on his face, for he was clad in a full suit of armor. Suddenly he flung his arms into the air, shuddered, and vanished beneath the churning waves. As if in a dream he reached out and offered the mirror to the hermit.

"Wait," said the old man. "Is there anything else you wish to see?"

"Yes," replied Lehndorf, who had partially recovered from his shock by this time. "Show us something that is happening now."

"Look into the mirror again," directed the hermit.

Hurrying to the side of his friend Bosch, Lehndorf stared at the mirror. As the mist cleared they saw a pigeon lying dead, a piece of cloth tied to one of its legs.

33

"What does that mean?" asked Lehndorf.

"On the cloth hanging from the dead bird's leg is a message for you. When you leave the cave, follow the Dog Star for one hundred paces. There you will find what you seek."

"How do you know these things?" demanded Bosch. "And how is it that you speak our language so well?"

"Ask no more questions," answered the old man, "but mark well my words. Once I was called Eberhard; that is all I will say of myself. Now, if you will rescue a friend in need, do as I have bid you. Hurry before it is too late."

There was a note of urgency in the hermit's voice as he dismissed the two crusaders, and so with no further words they hastened from the cave. Neither man spoke, for each had yet to absorb fully the impact of his own grim future; yet both were determined to locate the dead bird and find the message that would lead them to the rescue of a friend. It took only minutes to find what they were after, and when they examined the cloth with the message on it they knew that the friend was their old-time companion, Hans von Rudesheim.

"Thank God, he is alive!" exclaimed Lehndorf. "We must storm his prison and rescue him at dawn."

34

Within an hour the crusaders' encampment was buzzing with excitement, and by sunrise a heavily armed band of them was galloping at full speed to meet the enemy. Unfortunately, Saracen spies had alerted a large troop of warriors to the impending German attack. The town was ringed with defenders, and when the opposing forces met they fought each other savagely. As the morning wore on amidst the clanking and crashing of steel against steel, the curses and shouts of the living mingled with the cries and groans of the wounded and dying. At length the Prussian knights routed the enemy, and as they went about the sad business of seeing to their casualties, one man in particular felt cold chills run down his back despite the blistering heat. The man was Wilhelm Bosch. He had seen his friend Kurt Lehndorf lose his head and his life with the single sweep of a Saracen blade, just as Lehndorf's death had been predicted in the mirror of the hermit. Now, as the dust of battle was settling, Bosch gazed grimly on the dead body of another whose untimely end had been forecast. Rudolf Schramm lay motionless on the ground, a lance protruding from his chest.

The rescue of von Rudesheim was accomplished with little further effort. He was sick and emaciated from the ordeal of his imprisonment, however, and was ordered to return to Germany. As he was unfit to travel alone, Rudesheim's commander ordered that Wilhelm Bosch escort him back and see to their mutual safety on the trip.

Meanwhile, as von Rudesheim and his companion Bosch were making the lengthy and perilous journey from the Holy Land to Germany, Margaret, von Rudesheim's lovely flaxen-haired daughter, had met Graf Ulrich von Redlich, a handsome young nobleman, and the two had fallen deeply in love.

By the time von Rudesheim reached Germany, Margaret and Ulrich had decided to get married, and only awaited the arrival of her father to procure his paternal blessings. There seemed to be no earthly reason why he should disapprove in any way, but it was unthinkable at that time for people of their station in life to marry without parental approval.

Several days of feasting and rejoicing had been planned to celebrate von Rudesheim's homecoming, and there were so many guests present that the returning crusader took little notice of von Redlich until the second day. In the late afternoon von Rudesheim, while strolling in the garden, came across the two lovers locked in an embrace beneath a bower of blossoms.

Enraged at the sight he challenged von Redlich

and demanded to know who he was and what he was doing in Margaret's arms. Margaret, however, answered for him. "He is my fiancé, dear Father," she said, "and we have vowed to become man and wife."

"What?" roared von Rudesheim, his face turning livid with rage. "That can never be! I swore a solemn oath while rotting in a Saracen dungeon that if ever I was freed I would place you in a convent as a token of my gratitude to God! How dare you expect me to break my vow?"

"But, Father," she protested. "What about *our* vows? Are they any less solemn than yours? Surely the good Lord would not expect you to keep such a vow. You were not yourself when you made it!"

"Silence!" roared von Rudesheim. "You are going to the convent in the morning. No von Rudesheim has ever broken a vow to man or Heaven, and thus shall it ever be!"

"But I am a von Rudesheim too!" protested Margaret.

Angered at the logic of her argument, the angry knight slapped his daughter across the face and turned to her lover. "As for you, sir," he snarled, "I expect you to be out of this district within twenty-four hours or I shall . . ."

"I refuse!" retorted Ulrich defiantly.

37

In the face of such a challenge to his authority, von Rudesheim seized his daughter bodily and began dragging her away. Seeing her scream and struggle, von Redlich intervened and attempted to free her. Blinded by rage, von Rudesheim drew his dagger and stabbed the young man twice, fatally wounding him. Horrified to the point where reason fled, Margaret screamed hysterically, dashed to a parapet overlooking the Rhine, and plunged into the water several hundred feet below.

"Miserable, traitorous child!" cried von Rudesheim. "You have betrayed me! May your spirit haunt the waters where you have perished for all eternity!"

"And may mine join hers," gasped the dying Ulrich von Redlich, "for where she goes so will I go!" Then struggling to raise a blood-drenched hand, he pointed a finger at von Rudesheim and croaked, "Vile, murderous wretch! For your cruelty and vice may the powers of Hell itself rise up from the river and drag you bodily to eternal damnation. . . . And so that future generations shall remember your dreadful deed, may the calm waters of the Rhine be forever turbulent at the spot where my loved one perished!" And with those words he collapsed and died.

Von Rudesheim stood motionless, the bloodstained dagger in his hand, swaying slightly to and fro, never knowing that at that very moment one of his dearest friends was dying. Wilhelm Bosch, who had accompanied him from the Holy Land, was on his way to the castle at the precise moment that Margaret plunged into the Rhine. Shocked at the sight and without stopping to think, he dived in to save her. Clad as he was in full armor, he barely reached midstream when the weight dragged him down to the bottom.

As for von Rudesheim himself, the end was very near. Exactly one week after the tragedy he fell victim to the dreadful curse uttered by the young man he had so ruthlessly killed. While standing on the banks of the Rhine brooding in the pale light of the full moon, the knight of the castle was lost in bitter reflections. According to the legend a hideous black shape resembling a giant, hairy crab with hellish glowing green eyes rose noiselessly from the river, crept resolutely to his side, then seized him in its ugly pincers, and dragged him shrieking into the river, never to be seen again.

And they say that even to this day, even when the weather is calm and not a breath of wind is blowing, the waters of the Rhine near where Rudesheim castle once stood still rage and churn around the rocks, and frequently two misty figures, one a knight in armor, the other a woman in a long flowing gown, can be seen clasped in an eternal embrace. Of course, there are those who say that there are no figures, that the sight is only light and shadow and spray playing tricks on the eyes. But there are others who insist that they are the restless spirits of Margaret and Ulrich, the doomed lovers who refused to be parted at any cost.

The Coruisk Horror

On the Isle of Skye off the west coast of
Scotland there is a wild and gloomy lake called
Loch Coruisk. The waters are murky and green.
On all sides there are craggy mountains that
make the lake resemble a great, rocky basin.
Overshadowing its grim dark waters are dangerous
precipices of the Cuillin, a mass of jagged moun-
tain dominating the view from both land and sea.
The deathly silence, the awesome grandeur, and
the fantastic shapes of the boulders and rocks
give Coruisk an aura of brooding dread unlike
anything anywhere else in the world.

Naturally such a place abounds with legends
and traditions of a fearsome and terrifying nature.

It is said that Loch Coruisk is both haunted and cursed, perhaps more so than any other place in the British Isles. But of all the restless phantoms believed to stalk its inhospitable shores the most dreadful are the shades of three beautiful young women whose lust for riches and vicious deeds brought about a terrible curse which even to this day hangs like an ominous cloud over Coruisk's greenish waters.

According to local tradition, it all began around four hundred years ago with three young sisters, Maura, Elspeth, and Gilda McGregor. Elspeth, the eldest, had flaming red hair, a pair of sparkling green eyes, and a complexion like fresh cream. Tall and willowy, she walked with queenly bearing. Gilda, the middle sister, was equally fair, but not as tall. She had long raven tresses and bright blue eyes. The youngest, Maura, was small and blonde, with the features of a pixie. So lovely were the three McGregor sisters, that every other woman on the Isle of Skye regarded them with envy. All the young men were secretly in love with them, knowing deep in their hearts that their chances were poor indeed. It was well known from one tip of the island to the other that the McGregor girls were a haughty trio, who had often publicly declared that when the time came for them to marry they would accept only those suitors who were handsome and rich.

Now in these times the Isle of Skye was a happy and carefree place. There were no wild animals about, nor were there robbers or high-waymen lurking in the dark to terrify or harm the inhabitants. For this reason it was not at all un-common for people to wander freely about in the woods, and the glens, and by the waters of the lakes both by day and by night. Gloomy Loch Coruisk, however, was an exception, for even then it had a bad name.

Early one evening, so the story goes, the three sisters, Maura, Elspeth, and Gilda, were sitting about chatting about this and that, when Elspeth suddenly made a face, stood up, and said, "I'm bored to tears. Nothing ever happens here. Can't we find something new and exciting to amuse us?"

"Suppose," said Gilda, lowering her voice and narrowing her eyes, "suppose we were to pay a visit to old Mother MacPhee?"

"Not the old witch who lives in the woods!" gasped Maura apprehensively.

"Why not?" returned Gilda. "She won't hurt us. Perhaps if we offer her a few pennies she will tell our fortunes."

Elspeth looked doubtful. "What would Father Michael say?" she replied, crossing herself quickly.

43

"Why should he say anything?" Gilda challenged. "If we keep it a secret he will never know about it."

"I suppose you're right," said Elspeth.

"That settles it," said Gilda. "Let's pay a visit to Mother MacPhee."

"I don't like the idea myself," said Maura, "but I'll come too. If anything evil happens, though . . ."

"Nothing can happen," interrupted Gilda. "Come on, it's getting dark."

With that the three sisters wrapped their shawls about their shoulders and set out to visit the old witch. The shadows were growing longer and the sky on the horizon was ablaze with brilliant red clouds — blood-red clouds. Laughing and giggling as they skipped through the thickening woods, the girls soon found themselves enveloped by darkness. Twisted branches surrounded them on all sides and clutched at their dresses like bony-fingered demons. Their cheerful laughter turned to nervous whispers and soon they crept along slowly, tightly clutching one another by the hands.

A sudden flapping of wings made them gasp aloud. They stopped in their tracks. A huge owl overhead hooted his disapproval at their presence, and they hurried on. Presently they made out the dim glimmer of light in a clearing just beyond the path. Quickening their pace they soon found themselves standing before a ramshackle hut, the yellowish light of candles flickering behind its windows. Gilda, the bravest of the three, went up and knocked at the door.

"Come in, Gilda McGregor," cackled a wheezy voice, "and bring your sisters with you."

"How did she know we were here?" murmured Maura.

"Never mind," said Elspeth. "Let's go in."

Seizing the doorknob in her hand, Gilda turned it and pushed. The hinges creaked in protest but the door swung in. Hesitantly, the three sisters walked inside. A strange and unfamiliar array of aromas met their nostrils. With wide-eyed fascination they surveyed the tiny room. It was cluttered with bottles and crocks, boxes, and shelves. Stuffed birds, mysterious-looking dolls, and indescribable things were crammed in every nook and corner. Seated before the hearth, stirring the contents of a steaming iron pot, was old Mother MacPhee. She wore a homespun wool wrapper, and had a great shock of scraggly white hair, long bulbous nose, and gleaming pale eyes that seemed to burn with an inner fire. Her lips were cracked, and when she opened her mouth four crooked, long yellow teeth were revealed.

Maura and Elspeth trembled at the sight of

45

the old hag, and even bold Gilda shrank back a bit.

"Heh, heh, heh!" cackled the old witch, rocking back and forth on her stool. "Do I ken the smell o' fear in the three bonnie lassies? Come, sit ye doon. I will not bite ye." She pointed to a bench along the far wall, and as soon as the girls had seated themselves she said, "Well now, lassies, what d'ye want from auld Mother MacPhee?"

"We want to know our futures," said Gilda, leaning forward. "We want you to tell our fortunes. . . ."

"And we'll give you a handful of pennies for it," added Elspeth.

The old woman chuckled hoarsely and held out her hand. Once the coins were in her grasp she dropped them into a pocket in the recesses of her wrapper and raised a long bony finger. "Very well," she began. "Ye shall know your futures. But there be but one way t' learn of them. Ye must go to the cliffs over Coruisk's dark waters and cast spells at midnight."

"At midnight!" gasped Elspeth. "We would never set foot on those dread shores at midnight."

The witch shrugged. "Then ye'll never ken the future. That's the end of it."

"There isn't another way?" asked Gilda.

"Not a one," declared the old woman.

For a brief moment there was silence, save for the crackling of the fire in the hearth, and the purring of Mother MacPhee's huge black cat as she stroked its glistening fur. Then, after a hurried conference, the sisters turned to Mother MacPhee. Elspeth, the oldest, spoke. "Very well," she said. "If you will teach us the spells we will go to Coruisk."

"So be it," said the witch. "Now pay close attention, for there can be no mistakes when it comes to casting spells."

For the next several hours the McGregor sisters sat huddled around their weird teacher as she instructed them in the proper pronunciation of the incantations. Once they had learned to pronounce the words without error she said, "Now mind my words well. Draw a circle on the ground and prepare a fire in the midst of it." She took a stick and inscribed a circle in the dirt on the floor to show them the proper size, then she gave them several packets of powders, reminding them that they must be boiled in a pot during the chanting of the incantations. Then as an afterthought she handed them a small parchment pouch saying, "If nothing happens when ye have finished, throw this into the fire. . . . Now leave me!" With that they were dismissed.

The path from the witch's hut to Coruisk was

rocky and overgrown with brambles. The hooting
of owls and the howling of dogs in the distance
sent shivers down the girls' backs, but by now
they were so determined that nothing could keep
them from their rendezvous with the future. Finally they emerged from the thicket and reached
a clearing. There before them was the lake. Pale
flecks of silver, reflecting a thin crescent moon
above, shimmered in the dark waters. The dark
craggy mountains all around gave Coruisk the
look of a crater. For a moment they stood and
looked out across the waters. It was still as a
tomb. Not a breath of air stirred, not a creature
cried out. No grave could have been more silent.

Walking cautiously out onto a small flat preci-
pice directly overlooking the lake, Elspeth, Gilda,
and Maura looked at each other in the pale moonlight. They were gripped by terror, and at no
time during their strange adventure was their re-
solve at a lower ebb. But something forced them
to continue. They had to know their futures.
Wordlessly they drew the circle and kindled the
fire. As they chanted the strange-sounding words
of the incantation their fears left them. Next, according to the witch's instructions, they placed
the little pot over the fire and boiled the evil-
smelling concoction she had prepared for them.
Still nothing happened.

Finally, just as their patience was at its very end, Gilda said, "Wait! We have one more chance. . . ."

"Yes," interrupted Elspeth, "the pouch of parchment."

"I have it!" cried Maura.

"Then quickly, throw it into the fire!" declared Elspeth.

Rising to her feet, Maura drew forth the small pouch and tossed it onto the flames. They flared up with a distinct sizzling sound, then without warning the entire area surrounding them seemed to be illuminated by an eerie greenish light.

"Dear God, look!" cried Maura, pointing directly in front of her and slightly beyond the green glow of the light.

There, gradually taking shape before their eyes, was a shadowy figure vaguely like a man but much taller, perhaps seven feet or more. As it grew clearer they could make out a pair of baleful green glowing eyes. On the apparition's head was either a strange kind of crown or perhaps horns. It was hard to see exactly what the being was for its appearance remained indistinct, like something viewed through billowing smoke.

For a moment that seemed to the girls like an eternity they clung together, trembling and staring at the figure, which stared back at them

49

wordlessly. Then, still without moving it began to speak in a voice of silvery mellow tones. "Well, my pretty lassies?" it said mockingly.

"Who are you?" demanded Gilda, taking courage.

"I am the one you all seek," replied the apparition.

"What do you mean by that?" asked Elspeth.

"You have summoned me," it answered. "You wish something of me. Speak."

"We wish to know what our futures will be," said Elspeth.

"That is as it should be," declared the figure, "for I am as much a part of your futures as I am even now part of your present. But let us talk of another kind of present — the bonnie kind that lassies love — the gauds, the bangles, and the baubles. Would you like bracelets of gold to encircle your pretty wrists?"

"Indeed we would," replied Elspeth without hesitation.

"As I thought," said the horned figure. "You could not have answered otherwise. Very well then, if you do exactly what I demand of you the golden bracelets will be yours on the morrow."

"What must we do?" exclaimed Maura, speaking up for the first time.

"You must swear never to reveal what has

happened here this night between us. Do you understand?"

"We understand," murmured the sisters in chorus.

"Then swear!"

"We swear."

The strange being uttered a low, chilling chuckle, then said, "Excellent. Now hear me well. One month from now, at the same hour, you will return to this spot with a living creature. You will cast the same spells you cast tonight, then you will kill the living creature and throw it into the lake."

"What sort of creature must we bring?" gasped Elspeth.

The figure chuckled again. "It makes no difference, lassies, as long as it lives, and breathes, and feels. Now, swear again that you will do exactly as I bid."

"We swear," murmured the sisters.

And at that precise instant there was a blinding flash of lightning followed by a long, unnatural silence. The girls rubbed their eyes, looked about, and saw that they were now alone.

They had had enough adventure for one night so they hurried home as fast as they could travel. By the time they got there and into their beds they were exhausted and sleep came quickly.

The following morning, with the light of the sun filling their house, they began to wonder if what they had experienced the night before was real or imagined. But when they found a small package outside the door addressed to them, and when upon opening it, they found three golden bracelets fashioned in the shape of serpents, they knew that everything had happened exactly as they recalled it.

This, of course, was the beginning of their road to doom. At the end of the month they awoke on the appointed day and went out to find a living victim for their weird benefactor. It had been their intention to find a rat or a mouse but, unable to catch either, they chose instead a helpless kitten. Driven by a passion for the forbidden, they returned to dread Coruisk's gloomy shores, strangled the kitten, cast the spells, and summoned the mysterious horned one. He was pleased with their obedience, and promised them still more fine presents if they would continue to do his bidding. They readily agreed, for though they had the faces of angels, their hearts and soul were corrupted by a lust for treasure, and they were no longer what they appeared to be.

The following day they were rewarded by three more golden bracelets, delivered to their doorstep by unseen hands. They were beside themselves with excitement, so much so that they could hardly contain themselves for another month. They began scheming as to what their next victim should be, and finally decided on a chicken or a duck.

After several months the McGregor sisters began to tire of their golden bracelets. They wanted something more beautiful, more valuable. "Why don't we ask for purses of gold?" suggested Gilda. "Then we can buy whatever we wish."

On the next midnight meeting with the horned one they made known their desire for money. "To be sure, lassies. If it is money you want, then it is money you shall have. But you will have to kill on a grander scale than mere chickens and cats. Mark me well now, the greater your victims, the greater my gifts. Now leave me!" With these words he faded into the gloom.

Now, as the months passed, the three sisters rarely smiled or laughed. By day they would count and fondle their newly acquired riches; by night they would scheme and plot over what or who their future victims would be. In time they built themselves a grand house, and though everyone on the Isle of Skye wondered where their wealth came from, no one dreamed there was any connection between the McGregor sisters and the regular disappearances of dogs, sheep, and finally unwanted children and helpless old people.

After several years the three sisters were unquestionably the most wealthy women on the island, if not in all Scotland. Now they wanted something money could not buy: They wanted husbands who were richer than they, as well as handsome and loving. So one night they asked the horned one if he might fulfill this desire, and he assured them that it would be done.

Within days three foreign noblemen were shipwrecked on the Isle of Skye. They were young, handsome, and rich beyond measure. They courted the McGregor sisters and married them shortly afterwards amidst great pomp and ceremony. For a time the girls were deliriously happy, and for three months never once set foot on Coruisk's gloomy shores. Then one day their husbands suggested that they leave the Isle of Skye for the lands of their own forefathers. Not knowing that they were in the grip of something far more powerful than their marriage vows the sisters refused. From cheerful brides they turned into screaming, quarrelsome harpies. Finally one night, on the pretense of making up again, they lured their unsuspecting husbands to the shores of Coruisk and cold-bloodedly murdered them.

One thing they had never counted on was the possibility of a witness to their deeds. Never had a living soul observed any of their terrible crimes. But there is a first time for everything. Barely an instant had passed after they killed their husbands when they heard a rustling in the bushes just beyond the clearing. Rushing to the spot they suddenly found themselves face to face with old Mother MacPhee.

"So," cackled the old witch. "Ye've come a long way since I first sent ye doon the long path tae drear Coruisk. I wonder what your friends would say if they could see ye now!"

"But they never will know!" hissed Elspeth, raising her dagger.

In a flash the three sisters pounced on the old woman, snarling like beasts as they attacked. Then stepping back and assuming her to be dead they prepared to lift her lifeless body and hurl it into the murky waters. But to their amazement she was still alive. Raising a bloody hand and pointing her finger accusingly, she croaked hoarsely, "Stupid wenches, in turning on me you have destroyed your last chance of escape. I curse you! I curse you till the end of eternity. Soon you will meet the same fate as those you have cruelly murdered. Then it will be your doom to haunt these dread shores forever alongside the Evil One himself whom you have been serving since your first wicked deed!"

Then she gasped and died. "Good riddance!" declared Gilda. "Come, let's throw her stinking carcass into the lake."

The deed accomplished, they returned to their home and fell into deep, dreamless sleep.

For a short while thereafter, they continued their career of unbridled evil, but just as the witch had predicted, it finally came to an end. They made the mistake of choosing an old gardener for a victim. He had a nephew who was suspicious of them, especially when he heard that they had invited the old man to dine with them one night. Gathering up a few friends, the youth confided his suspicions and followed the uncle to the McGregor house.

When the four young men saw the sisters take the old man out of the house an hour before midnight they knew something was amiss. Laughing gaily the three sisters led their intended victim, now staggering with drink, to a small cart, and began their grim journey to Coruisk — totally unaware it would be their last.

By the time they reached the scene of their crimes the old man was sound asleep, lulled to slumber by the wine and the jogging motion of the cart. He was going to be the easiest victim they ever had — or so they thought. But before they were able to raise their daggers, the young men leaped from their hiding places, disarmed the shrieking sisters, and hurled them into the dark waters of the lake, after wresting a confession from Maura, the youngest.

Soon after, it was reported that nightly three beautiful phantoms could be seen by the waters of Coruisk, weeping, sighing, moaning, and groaning, and looking for fresh victims to lure to their deaths. And it is said that even to this day the shores of this wild and gloomy lake are haunted still by the accursed sisters, restlessly stalking the darkness waiting for the final judgment day.

The Curse of
the Shepherd

There is an old Spanish legend dating back to the days of the Moorish presence. It is a legend about a poor peasant boy, a shepherd, who for very good reasons invoked a curse upon a queen. These were troubled times in Spain, half of the country was Christian and half, Moorish. These were the days before the legendary El Cid, days of warfare, strife, and danger.

At the time the story begins, a powerful Moorish caliph named Al-Mansur was the king of Córdoba. The most successful of all Moorish rulers, it was his sword that carried the crescent of Islam to its peak of glory. He was hated and feared by his Christian adversaries with whom he was intermittently at war.

The city of Burgos, capital of the kingdom of Castile, nearly seven hundred kilometers to the north, was ruled by a Christian count, Don Fernando Gonzales, whose reputation as a warrior was not to be scorned. Count Gonzales' principal problem was his wife, Doña Ava, whose singular lack of morals was the gossip of the city.

One night during the heat of the summer, a young peasant boy named Miguel was driving a flock of sheep from their long day of grazing back to the farm where he was employed as a shepherd. He was out so late because several of his flock had strayed and he did not dare go home without all his sheep. He eventually rounded up the last stray and was homeward bound when he came upon a clearing in the woods that, despite the late hour, seemed so appealing to his woolly charges that they spread out and began grazing once more.

This offered no problem to him other than a brief loss of time, which hardly bothered him because time was the one thing he had in abundance. Having been out in the open long after sundown, Miguel's eyes had grown quite accustomed to the dark. In the clearing it hardly seemed to be night because there was a brilliant moon that bathed everything in a silvery flood of soft, pale light. Beyond the clearing was a clump of low bushes, and beyond that Miguel thought he saw a strange glint of light flashing.

Being a simple youth who had no cause to fear anything, his curiosity overcame him and he went over to see if he could discover what the flash had been. By the time he reached the bushes, however, caution returned and he dropped to his knees, then proceeded noiselessly on until he was able to poke his head out on the far side. The instant he saw what had attracted his attention he drew in his breath. There, standing at the edge of a cliff, was a tall handsome man in gleaming armor. He stood there quietly, his arms folded across his chest, head back, feet apart. He gazed up into the sky as if he were counting the stars or trying to communicate with the moon.

Miguel knew that what he had seen was the reflection of moonbeams on the man's armor, but he could hardly believe his eyes when he recognized the sad, handsome face of the noble figure before him. It was Count Fernando Gonzales, the King of Castile.

Suddenly, as the shepherd gazed awestruck, he noticed a shadow moving toward the count. An instant later there emerged from the darkness a giant of a man, a Moor, clad in golden chain mail and armor, a spiked helmet on his head. He rushed up behind the unsuspecting Spaniard, seized him, and hurled him over the cliff. The unfortunate count had barely time to cry out before it was over. The Moor paused long enough to look over the cliff, then turned and disappeared in the direction from which he came. But in the brief moment he stood there in the moonlight Miguel saw his face and knew he would never forget it as long as he lived.

Trembling in terror the youth cringed in the darkness, barely able to believe what he had seen. Finally he went back to his flock and began to drive them home. He was heartsick, outraged, and filled with a feeling of helplessness. After all, he was a poor, illiterate peasant. What could he do to avenge the murder of the Lord of Burgos?

Unfortunately, Miguel did not have long to think of such things because less than an hour after he left the scene of the crime he was himself seized by a band of roving bandits. The Spanish countryside was a treacherous place in those days. Between warring factions of Spaniards and Moors, there were wandering gangs of robbers and highwaymen scourging the land like plagues of noxious insects. They were cutthroats and thieves to whom murder and torture were everyday diversions.

Miguel had no false illusions about his future when he was taken. Fortunately he was a healthy, strapping lad, and upon being dragged back to the bandits' camp and thrown to the ground before their chieftain, he was given a choice between life and death. This was a gesture of generosity on the part of the chieftain who was feeling mellowed by the wine he was drinking and pleased at having acquired such a fine flock of sheep without the loss of one man. His offer was simple: Miguel could either become part of the robber band or be hanged from a tree.

Life among the bandits was no bed of roses for the unfortunate shepherd. Given only the most menial of tasks, he was beaten, abused, taunted, and generally forced to live a miserable life. Only one person made his lot tolerable. She was a girl about his age named Manuela. She would talk to him, help him with his chores, and secretly bring him better food when he was given leftovers. It was she who finally persuaded the others to treat Miguel like a human being instead of a beast. He had explained to her that though he had never intended to become a bandit, he accepted the fact that he must now become one of them because there was no turning back. He had no family, the farmer for whom he had worked probably assumed that he had made off with the flock of sheep and would have him hanged as a thief if he ever came back, and so there was no other course left open for him.

It was shortly after his acceptance by the bandits that Miguel was given his first important task. It was decided to send him to Burgos on a spying mission. He was to determine the exact date that a certain wealthy merchant would leave for Madrid with a shipment of valuable goods. He was also to learn which route the merchant's party would travel.

Though he could neither read nor write, Miguel was a very bright young man and he obtained the information he had been sent to get in less than three days' time. He was on his way back to the bandit encampment when he was stopped by a richly dressed woman, who offered him a gold coin to deliver a letter for her to the palace of the late king.

Miguel accepted, and as he made his way through the crowded streets he quickly realized it was no ordinary day. There were strolling musicians, crowds of people laughing and singing, streamers and banners hanging from the houses, and flowers everywhere. Brilliantly woven coats of arms were displayed on the villas of the nobles, and, in an unusual display of peace and harmony,

63

the Moorish crescent was as visible as the Christian cross.

In comparison to the richly garbed townspeople Miguel, in his homespun rustic garb, was a minor curiosity, and he attracted some attention as he edged his way through the merrymaking crowds. When he finally reached the gates of the palace he saw at once by the look on the guards' faces that he would not be welcomed with open arms. Calling upon his quick wit, he held up the letter given him by the lady. The sight of its seal brought instant recognition, and Miguel was admitted at once.

The actual delivery of the letter was an easy matter, but as he began to leave he found himself swept away by the beauty of the palace grounds. Before he knew what had happened he lost his way and quite unexpectedly found himself in the midst of a clump of shrubs at the edge of a secluded garden. The sound of voices attracted his attention and, crouching low, he moved stealthily forward in order to catch a glimpse of the speakers.

They were seated on a marble bench, their backs toward him, and the sight of their rich clothes dumbfounded Miguel. Never in his life had he seen such garments — velvet, silk, and brocade, encrusted with jewels and silver and gold. But he was especially awestruck by the beautiful, graceful hands of the lady. Her fingers were long, tapered, and bedecked with sparkling rings. The man was a giant of a figure, clad in golden armor that was intricately etched with a silvertraced design. Suddenly he turned slightly to embrace the lady and in that instant Miguel caught sight of his face. He was so shocked that he almost cried out. It was Al-Mansur, the Moorish king of Córdoba, and the murderer of Count Gonzales.

By exercising every ounce of strength and willpower he possessed, Miguel managed to retreat. Then as fast as he could, he ran to the palace gates. The sight of a poorly clad peasant boy running like a thief aroused the suspicion of the first palace guards, and he was arrested. They quickly learned that he had stolen nothing, and when they questioned him further he told them exactly what he had seen, the King of Córdoba in the arms of a Spanish lady. Furthermore, he told them that he had witnessed that same man murder the King of Castile. At first they were skeptical, but he was taken before a priest where he swore that everything he said was the truth. As he was being questioned about the identity of the lady, it soon became apparent that she was Doña Ava, the unfaithful widow of the slain Count Gonzales.

After finishing their interrogation the palace guards assured Miguel that they believed every word he had said, then sent him on his way with a warning not to say a word to anyone else. The uneasy politics of the time made it impossible to act decisively in every instance. Miguel could not understand such complicated matters, but he was pleased to escape with his life. One thing he knew: Had the Moor seen him he would never have left the garden alive.

Unfortunately the soldiers who had questioned Miguel had loose tongues, loosened even more, no doubt, by strong drink during the festivities. In any event they told their cronies what had happened between their queen and the King of Córdoba, and within a few days it was common gossip throughout the whole of Burgos. Naturally the word reached Doña Ava, who was infuriated. Enlisting the aid of her henchmen and spies she soon learned the identity of the country lad who had witnessed her indiscretion and reported it.

In a matter of weeks he was tracked down, captured, and dragged back to the palace at Burgos. There he was thrown into a dungeon and savagely beaten, then informed that he would be publicly executed the following day. As he lay in his cell awaiting the dawn of his final day, Miguel could not erase from his mind the picture of Doña Ava's beautiful hands. When the priest came to hear his confession and grant final absolution, the youth begged to be granted a final glimpse of the queen before he died. His request was refused and he was laughed at by his jailors.

As the long hours of the night ticked slowly away, and Miguel saw with the gradually lightening sky that his life was soon to be snuffed out, bitterness welled up in his heart. Seizing a cellmate by the shoulder, he shook the man and cried out, "I curse this woman! She is evil; she is a witch! May her hands be as fatal to her as they have been to me! I curse her! I curse her!"

Now, it happened that the man to whom Miguel spoke was a poet, who was languishing in the dungeon for no greater crime than writing and speaking the truth. He knew that the trembling lad before him could neither read nor write, so he said, "My young friend, I will see to it that your words are not forgotten. May the punishment of Almighty God fall upon this wicked woman's head." And before the doomed shepherd was taken away he saw the words of his curse inscribed upon the dungeon wall.

At this time Don Sancho Gonzales, the son of the late King of Castile, had recently reached his majority and the day was approaching for him to ascend the throne of his late father. Until his actual coronation, however, Doña Ava, as queen regent, held the reins of government firmly in her lovely hands. No man in Spain was more aware of the situation than Al-Mansur, the King of Córdoba. The crucial moment in his plan to raise the crescent of Islam over all of Spain was now at hand. Up to now everything had worked perfectly — the winning of Doña Ava's heart, the assassination of her husband. Now it was time for the Moorish warrior king to play his final hand.

During a secret rendezvous with Doña Ava, Al-Mansur made his proposal. "My love," he said, "take my hand in marriage, and as we unite our hearts, we will unite our kingdoms under the glorious banner of Islam."

Her eyes widened. "Abandon my faith!" she exclaimed.

"There is only one true God," replied Al-Mansur. "Allah, the merciful, the beneficent, the giver of life, the creator of all things."

Doña Ava was so blinded to all but her love for him that with a single word she agreed. At that point he knew that she would do anything he demanded of her, and that was when he revealed his ultimate requirement. Only one obstacle stood in the way of his design, and that obstacle was Don Sancho, Doña Ava's son.

"He must die," declared Al-Mansur. "And he

must die by your hand, thus will I be certain of your loyalty to me."

She was appalled. She faltered, not knowing what to say. She loved her son, but she was a virtual slave to the Moor. More sure of himself than ever, he gave her no time to answer. "Make up your mind, madam," he said. "You have an hour to decide." And with that he left the room.

For most of the hour the tormented queen found her conscience locked in combat with her passions, and in the end her passions won. A plan was made in which she would poison Don Sancho by handing him a specially prepared cup of wine at a great banquet due to take place in three days.

On the night of the banquet all the nobles of Córdoba and Castile were gathered together. It was a festive occasion, when Moslem and Christian were to pledge their friendship and agree to live in harmony and love. The plot against young Don Sancho's life had been worked out to the last detail. A palace servant had been given poison to place in a cup of wine. He was told that it was medicine for the queen. After the crime had been committed he was to be accused of murder, arrested, and promptly executed. It would happen so fast that the poor wretch would never have an opportunity to plead his innocence.

The banquet was in full sway. There were

laughter and singing as musicians serenaded the guests. Jugglers and magicians performed feats of entertainment. Only Doña Ava remained aloof and grim-faced amidst the merriment and good fellowship. Her heart beat rapidly and her hands trembled, for though she had done many evil things in her lifetime, she had never murdered, and as she prepared to take the life of her only son a cold chill enveloped her. The unsuspecting young man sat beside her, smiling, talking and joking, never dreaming that the silver goblet of wine before him contained enough deadly poison to kill ten men.

The grand toast of the evening was just minutes away. The deadly goblet seemed to shimmer and grow as Doña Ava stared at it in fascination. Then suddenly, something caught her attention, a hand movement, a tinkling laugh. She averted her gaze from the goblet and looked down the table where her lover, Al-Mansur, was seated beside a certain Doña Isabella de Molina, a beautiful woman of twenty. His arm encircled her waist, and into her hand he pressed a folded piece of paper. Doña Ava could hardly believe her eyes. Before her very eyes the wretch was betraying her. At that instant her love became burning hatred. Only one thought dominated her mind: Revenge! Rising abruptly to her feet she pointed her finger at the Moor and screamed at the top of her voice, "Murderer! Murderer! This is the man who murdered my husband, but he will not take my son's life! He will not!"

With that she seized the poisoned wine and raised it to her lips, draining the goblet to the last drop. Thus, with the eyes of all fixed on her in astonishment she uttered a final bloodcurdling shriek, and slumped lifeless across the table. In this fashion the shepherd's curse was fulfilled and she died by her own hand. In the confusion Al-Mansur slipped away unnoticed, raging with frustration at the collapse of his grandiose dreams of empire.

The Curse of
the Gypsy

Some years ago a very proper Londoner named Anthony Davis lived with his family in a fashionable section of the city. They were a fairly well-to-do family. Davis had an important position in the Inland Revenue Office, his son, Charles, was a senior at Oxford; and his pretty daughter, Elizabeth, was engaged to marry an extremely wealthy young man named John Hewitt. All in all then, the overall future of the Davis family looked rosy indeed.

It so happened that Mr. Davis was a great walker, and in order to walk precisely three miles per day, a distance he believed to be most ideal for the preservation of health, he arose early every morning and walked from his house to his office which was located just off the Strand and

within a short distance of Waterloo Bridge. One
morning as he was walking along the Victoria
Embankment beside the river Thames he was
accosted by a shabbily dressed woman with wild
black hair, luminous dark eyes, and a thread-
bare red shawl. Approaching him with her right
palm upturned and her hand outstretched she
said, "Won't you give a ha'penny to poor Luisa
the gypsy? Only a copper ha'penny, that's nothing to a fine gent like yourself."

Indeed, a halfpenny was nothing to Mr. Davis,
but he considered himself to be a man of high
moral principles. He contributed generously each
year to the Fund for Heathen Orphans and the
Anti-Vice League, two worthy organizations he
felt more than adequately fulfilled his charitable
obligations. He was also a dues-paying member
of the Society to Abolish Street Begging, a group
whose cardinal rule was to discourage the practice
by never giving so much as a bent farthing to any
mendicant, regardless of age, sex, or condition.
Under the circumstances, without slowing his
pace, he curtly dismissed the gypsy and continued
on his way. Assuming that he had left her behind
he was mildly annoyed after a few moments to
hear footsteps behind him and then to feel a tug
at his sleeve from the rear. It was the gypsy
again. "Only a ha'penny," she insisted. "You

wouldn't refuse a poor woman now, would you?"

Losing his temper, Davis shook her loose, spun around on his heel, and exclaimed, "Damn you, woman! Leave me in peace or I shall call a constable."

She drew in her breath sharply and cried, "Oh, so you would curse me then. . . ." and in a voice that was strangely commanding said, "Look me in the eye, sir!"

Davis could not help himself, and did as he was told. At first glance he had thought she was an elderly woman, but on looking more closely he could see that she was not more than thirty, if that. Her dark eyes flashed angrily in a glare that was unmistakably malevolent. Her hands held defiantly on her hips and her mouth twisted into a wicked-looking snarl. She pointed a long and grimy finger in his face and declared, "Mark well what I say, unhappy man. I fling your curse back and add my own. May it rest heavy on you and yours. You will see me three times more before you die, and upon each occasion there will be suffering in your house."

The woman's manner was so disconcerting that Davis regretted at once his hasty words and a cold chill shot down his spine. "Look here, my good woman," he said, hastily digging into his pocket. "There's no need for us to part with bad blood.

Let's both admit we lost our tempers, and part on good terms." With that he took a silver florin and offered it to her. But instead of taking it she pushed his hand aside and sent the coin spinning to the ground.

"It's too late for that, my haughty friend," she sneered. "You can't buy me with silver now. The die is cast! A curse has been met with a curse and nothing can change it." And without another word she threw her shawl around her shoulders, turned, and stalked away in the opposite direction.

For a moment or two Davis stood there watching her, then he shook his head and continued on to his office. It was a disturbing incident, and even though he took no stock in gypsy fortune-tellers, spiritualists, and other such things, he could not help but be disturbed. To begin with he was annoyed for having lost control of himself, even for that brief moment. He was even more annoyed for allowing the whole silly business to bother him. After all, what was the woman but a dirty illiterate with a malicious heart and a vicious tongue. Yet, try as he might he was unable to banish the image of the gypsy from his thoughts for the rest of the day.

That night when he got home, he told his wife all about the disquieting experience. Seeing that he was genuinely upset about it, Mrs. Davis did

everything she could to persuade him there was
nothing for him to be alarmed about and that the
most sensible thing to do was to forget the matter
altogether. But when he went to bed that night he
could not sleep. As he lay tossing and turning in
the dark he kept reliving his encounter with the
gypsy, wishing desperately each time that it
would have a different outcome, yet reliving it over
and over exactly as it had occurred. Even after
sleep finally came Davis was troubled by night-
mares in which he found himself encountering the
malevolent stare of the gypsy everywhere he
looked.

Although he said nothing of what was troubling him at breakfast he was still unable to erase
the unpleasant thoughts from his mind, and as
he hurried down the streets of London to his office, he trembled every time he heard footsteps
behind him, and the merest sound of a woman's
voice out of earshot caused him to feel a sinking
feeling in the pit of his stomach. Even after he
got to the office he kept hearing the words of the
gypsy's curse ringing in his ears until he began
to fear that he was losing his mind.

Fortunately, as the days became weeks, Davis
thought less and less of the gypsy and her stinging
curse. What he had feared at first to be the
beginning of a dangerous obsession gradually

faded from his mind and in time he thought nothing more of the incident. Besides, he had more important, more pressing matters to occupy his time. Of the greatest concern was the state of his daughter's health. A fragile young woman at best, she had succumbed to a respiratory infection that was not helped by London's damp and clammy climate. Although she was presently in a state of outwardly seeming good health, she was in fact very susceptible to a dangerous relapse. Her doctor had recommended that she be sent to Spain or Italy until she regained her strength, but she had steadfastly refused, insisting that she wanted to remain in England in order to be near her fiancé, John Hewitt. Fearing to argue with her and risk the danger of her becoming over-excited, her parents, against their better judgment, had agreed to let her remain at home.

One Saturday in early spring, Hewitt invited his future father-in-law to lunch with him at his club, and to discuss plans for the upcoming wedding. It was a relatively uneventful but pleasant afternoon and when they left the club they took a taxi, Hewitt intending to drop Davis off on his way home. As they were driving past the British Museum the driver suddenly swerved to avoid hitting a woman who unexpectedly stepped off the curb. The vehicle struck a lamp post with such force that Hewitt was thrown to the street and knocked unconscious. Davis suffered a broken arm, and as he struggled to the side of his injured young companion he glanced up and his blood ran cold. There, bending over the prostrate form was the woman who had stepped from the curb — it was Luisa, the gypsy. As she looked up into Davis's face there was a glint of recognition in her eyes. There came such a malevolent expression on her face that Davis almost cried out. However, at that moment a crowd began to gather and she slipped away and disappeared.

Both Davis and young Hewitt were hospitalized for a short while, though neither was seriously injured. Davis's daughter, however, on hearing what had happened to her father and fiancé, fell into a deep depression and slept very fitfully on the night of the accident. There was no central heating in the house, as was common in England at the time, and sleeping without sufficient bed covering she contracted pneumonia; for over a week she hovered between life and death. Meanwhile both her father and her fiancé were released from the hospital.

As soon as Hewitt was able to visit he rushed to her bedside. He was only permitted to remain in the room for a few minutes and the poor girl was so disappointed she collapsed into a fit of coughing and weeping. Thoroughly disturbed at this turn of events Mrs. Davis, who remained in the room, asked her husband to pull down the windowshade while she rearranged the covers on the bed and attempted to comfort the unhappy girl.

Without answering, Davis went over to the window where he casually glanced out before pulling down the shade. He felt a tightening in his chest. There on the street below stood Luisa, the gypsy. The wind was blowing her long black hair and her tattered red shawl streamed out behind her. She looked up and began laughing, with such a look of malice, that Davis almost tore the blind from the window. My God! he thought to himself, that's the second time I've seen her. What terrible thing now?

As if in direct answer to his agonized thought he heard a scream. It was his wife's. Rushing to the bedside of his daughter, he knew. The girl lay back motionless, her eyes staring lifelessly into space. She was dead.

Twice the curse had been fulfilled. An icy chill overcame the grief-stricken Davis. Next time it would be his turn. Like a man in a trance he went back to the window and lifted the shade. The gypsy was gone, but the picture of her burning eyes was indelibly engraved on his mind, and he silently asked himself how much time he had left.

In time, the pall of grief slipped away from the Davis household and life returned to normal. Davis's son, Charles, was graduated from Oxford, received an excellent appointment to the Foreign Office, and promptly got married. On the Christmas after the wedding the Davises gave an elaborate party in honor of the newlyweds and invited numerous friends and relatives. It was a festive occasion with all the trappings of the season, turkey and roast beef, suckling pig, fruits and candies, endless tankards of rich ale, and crystal goblets of wine. The assembled company were gathered about the roaring fire, some eating hot plum pudding, others sipping brandy, but a hush fell upon them as a wandering band of carolers paused outside to sing of the season's joys.

Suddenly, without warning, came a loud and ominous sound like that of a huge empty barrel rolling and bumping down the stairs from the upper part of the house. All conversation stopped, as well as all eating and drinking. The sound of the carols was forgotten as everyone present strained to listen, each person wondering what on earth the mysterious sound could be. It became louder and louder, though there was nothing to be seen, then it seemed to pass by and proceed in the direction of the kitchen, the door of which was suddenly thrown open as if blown by a heavy gust of wind.

The impact of the sound was so great that everyone in the room felt a deep sense of melancholy, although all tried to hide it at the time. No one spoke, and everyone with the exception of Davis himself stared furtively about as if seeking some sign or other in a neighbor's eyes that might explain what had happened. Those who were questioned afterwards recollected that Davis stood riveted to the spot, staring at the kitchen door, his jaw slack, his eyes wide and staring as if he were seeing an apparition.

Everyone remained in this temporary state of shock for a moment or two after the sound had ended, then they all began talking at once in an effort to resume the festivities. They went through the motions, they even sang carols, but somehow the earlier tone of high spirits was never reached again and soon afterwards the guests began to leave. At last Davis and his wife were alone. "It was that accursed gypsy," he said. "I don't know how she caused the disturbance, but I saw her open the kitchen door and come right into the room here. She didn't say a word, she just stood there mocking me with her eyes!"

Mrs. Davis didn't know what to say. She had

been there the whole time. She too had seen the kitchen door flung open, and she knew perfectly well that no one had come through it. "You couldn't possibly have seen her," she insisted. "I was right here beside you. It was the excitement. You must have imagined it."

"That's possible," he said softly, "but I don't know. All I can say is that I've seen her for the third time now, and I fear the worst."

"Let's not even think about it now," said Mrs. Davis. "We've had a long day and we should go to bed now. By morning the sun will be shining and we shall have forgotten all about your horrid gypsy."

"You're probably right," he said, inwardly not believing a word either of them had spoken. He knew what he had heard and he knew what he had seen. He sighed, wished his wife good-night, and retired.

The next morning was a glorious day. The sky was blue and the sun shone brightly through the windows. But Anthony Davis did not see the sunlight, for he was dead. When the doctor was summoned he hurried over and pronounced the cause of death to be heart failure. But Mrs. Davis knew otherwise. Her unfortunate husband had died a victim of the gypsy's curse.

The Curse of Moy

Centuries ago the clans of Scotland were far more active than they are today. They consisted of related families governed by a chief who exercised great power even to the point of life and death. Although there were kings who attempted to maintain their sovereignty, communication was extremely difficult. Because of the wild and rugged nature of the country, travel was highly dangerous and at times all but impossible. As a result the clans, who clung together for mutual protection and support, were independent to the point that their loyalties were virtually limited to their own.

For the most part they were fierce and war-like people, whose pride and arrogance frequently led them into serious trouble. Though they had a rigid sense of honor that would put most of the modern world to shame, they were also given to unspeakable acts of treachery which often led to long and bloody feuds that sometimes lasted for generations. Such a feud had been carried on for many years between the clans of Chattan and Grant, who lived amidst the craggy, barren peaks of Inverness in the north of Scotland.

At the time the events that are about to unfold occurred, the chief of Clan Chattan was the fearsome Macintosh, whose very name struck terror into the hearts of his enemies. His ancestral home was the castle of Moy, a nearly inaccessible fortress standing on a rock at the edge of Loch Moy, a deep, dark body of water surrounded on all sides by thick, nearly impenetrable forests of evergreens. It was thanks to Macintosh's treacherous duplicity that a terrible curse was called down upon him and his descendants. The dreadful details of how it came about, according to legend, were not revealed until a full sixty years had passed.

The occasion of this revelation was a festive celebration at the castle of Moy in honor of the present laird's recently born son and heir. Members of the clan had gathered from far and wide, along with friends, retainers, and favored tenants of the Macintosh estates. The air was filled with joyous sounds, laughter, singing, and the skirling of bagpipes. Wine flowed freely and banquet tables groaned beneath the weight of succulent roasts, rich puddings, and bursting pies. As the evening wore on the celebration grew wilder and the gloomy corridors of Moy castle echoed to the unfamiliar sounds of gaiety.

At the height of the revelry a somber black-clad figure stepped uninvited into the great hall where most of the merrymakers were gathered. At the sight of her the entire company fell silent, focusing their undivided attention on the elderly woman whose long white hair fell below her waist. Although she had never been known to harm anyone, she was nonetheless feared. A mysterious, solitary figure who dwelt in a hut high up on a lonely slope in wild Badenoch, the woman's presence was generally regarded as a harbinger of evil tidings. Consequently as she paused at the threshold and fixed her stare on Macintosh, the laird of Moy, a chill of apprehension filled every heart in the great hall. Then as she strode forward in the direction of the young chief there was a great scramble to clear the way before her.

Pausing not three paces in front of the laird she raised her arm and pointed a long tapering finger at him and called out in a clear loud voice, "Your revels are in vain: no heir of Moy shall rule its rocky precincts!" An expression of bewilderment mixed with horror came over young Macintosh's face and nervous murmurs arose from the assembled guests. Immediately, the old woman held up her hand to demand silence and again a hush fell over the hall. Then she told the terrible tale with which she alone had lived for the past sixty years.

After many years of feuding between the clans Chattan and Grant, Macintosh, chief of the Chattans, sent a communication to Urquhart, chief of the Grants. It was a proposal for a truce to discuss peace and an end to the years of bloodshed and violence. Urquhart readily agreed and a meeting was arranged to take place at the castle of Moy. Accompanying Urquhart on the mission of peace was Alvah, a young Grant chieftain who was betrothed to Fiona, Urquhart's daughter.

The meeting between the two clan chiefs was conducted with due cordiality, and at its conclusion a solemn oath was pledged by all that the Chattan-Grant feud had ended and that the two clans would enter into the bonds of friendship from that time on. It was well after dark when the meeting was over, and after ceremonial toasts had been drunk, Urquhart and Alvah left the castle of Moy to make their homeward journey.

They had to traverse the wild and desolate Badenoch region with its rocks and crags and dense thickets. It was very late and very dark when they reached the edge of a thickly wooded glen. Just as they were about to venture into it they heard the battle cry of the Chattans, and before they knew what had happened they found themselves surrounded by an armed band of Chattan warriors. Urquhart, being unarmed, prepared to fight with his bare hands, but Alvah drew his great two-edged sword and fought like a demon until he was finally overcome by the greater force of superior numbers.

Subdued and bound, the two Grants were taken to a forbidding prison on a rocky isle in the midst of Loch Moy and thrown into a deep reeking dungeon. Stunned and infuriated at having fallen victim to the treachery of Macintosh, Urquhart realized that the chief of the Chattans had arranged his capture for personal reasons. Some months earlier Macintosh had proposed a marriage to Fiona, Urquhart's beautiful daughter. Knowing that she despised the Chattan chief almost as much as she loved her fiancé, Alvah, Urguhart had ignored the offer. Now, however, he understood the reason for his capture so soon after the offer of peace. If word were spread that the clans had ended their feud, the way would be clear for Macintosh to marry Fiona. There remained only two obstacles in his path, her father and her fiancé. "I fear our days may be numbered, lad," said Urquhart to his young companion, for he knew the ways of his enemy, and he knew how easily his "disappearance" along with that of Alvah could be explained away.

However, Fiona learned what had happened, and in the naive hope that she could prevail upon Macintosh to release the two men, she went alone to the castle of Moy to plead her case in person. It was like a lamb venturing into a pack of hungry wolves. The chief of the Chattans could hardly believe his ears when a retainer came to tell him that Fiona Urquhart was there requesting a private audience with him. His feelings were mixed. He was furious that she had learned that her father and sweetheart were his prisoners, making it impossible for him to trick her into marriage. But he also reveled in the thought that she was there in his castle and at his complete mercy. He did not have to marry her. He could do what he wished with her and discard her whenever it suited him.

Making no attempt to disguise his motives, Macintosh bluntly told the young woman that only by surrendering to his every demand could she hope to save the life of a chosen loved one. "Only one will I permit to live," he declared gruffly. "Take your choice and stand by your word," he added, promising that she could see them once together before making up her mind the next day.

Disconsolate but resigned, she refused to surrender without at least a show of defiance. With both fists clenched she looked Macintosh directly in the eye and said, "I'll make no bargains with you until I see them with my own eyes. How do I even know that Alvah and my father still live?"

"She should be beaten for her insolence," muttered one of Macintosh's burly retainers.

"What else d'ye expect from the daughter of a chieftain?" observed Macintosh. "Take her tae the dungeon," he added, "and let her see them, then deliver her back tae me."

Without further ceremony, Fiona was conducted out of the castle, taken to a boat, and rowed to the rocky prison on the isle in Loch Moy. The dungeon was rank and damp, and crawling with loathsome vermin. Pools of stagnant water covered with green slime dotted its broken floor, and the only illumination came from smoking torches of burning pitch that cast eerie flickering lights in all directions.

Fiona's heart sank at the spectacle of her two

loved ones languishing there in such filth and misery; nevertheless, she thanked heaven they were still alive. It was only after the rusty iron door had banged shut behind her that she was able to feel a moment of relief. After a tearful reunion, the three exchanged details of how they had all come to be where they were at that precise time, and when her father heard the harsh terms of Macintosh's ultimatum, he insisted that she must choose Alvah. "I'm an old man," he said. "I have lived my life. But you two are young and have a future ahead. Don't throw it away."

It was agreed then that Fiona and Alvah should meet the following day at high noon on the moors of Badenoch. This they thought would allow time for both of them to be released from the clutches of Macintosh. Urquhart would permit no lamentations at his daughter's final parting from him, instead he urged that she and Alvah rejoice at the prospect of their forthcoming marriage. With that he rattled the cell door and summoned the jailer, announcing that it was time for his daughter to leave.

The prospect of what lay ahead between her departure from the prison and her rendezvous with Alvah the next day weighed heavy on Fiona's heart, but there was nothing for her to do but endure what she must.

In the morning, after what had seemed several eternities to Fiona she was permitted to depart, and with all due haste she made her way to the appointed meeting place, a majestic hillside overlooking the moors of Badenoch. When she arrived she sat on a jagged boulder, the breeze blowing her hair, and she awaited the arrival of her beloved, passing the time by counting the clouds as they drifted past on their journey to the horizons.

As the sun climbed steadily toward the zenith, heralding the approach of noon, Fiona's heart began pounding in anticipation. The mixture of powerful emotions within her was devastating and she wept both for sorrow and joy, sorrow at the prospect of never seeing her father again, and joy at the prospect of being reunited with the man she loved. Suddenly she heard the sound of someone approaching. It had to be Alvah, coming to meet her as he had promised. Jumping to her feet she whirled around to face him as he came to throw himself into her arms. Then she froze where she stood. Laughing and sneering as they came were four Macintosh henchmen bearing between them the bruised and bloody bodies of her father and Alvah. Horror stricken, she could do nothing but stand there and watch as they tossed the bodies before her and stalked off.

For a while the jolt from what had happened

91

was so intense that the unfortunate young woman could do nothing but stand and stare. But then, as the enormity of Macintosh's treachery sank in, and with the strength, energy, and endurance that is born of desperation, she began to gather rocks with which she built a cairn over the remains of her loved ones. Then as the sky turned purple in the wake of the setting sun she turned to face the direction of Moy castle. Raising her hands and clenching her fists, she shrieked in a voice that was barely human. She cursed the house of Moy and everyone loyal to it. She called upon the combined powers of Heaven and Hell to bring destruction and misery on Macintosh and his progeny. "Let their women weep as I weep," she cried. "Let them groan and suffer even as I suffer, and may no laird of Moy ever have a son to succeed him, to survive him, or to inherit his lands. May Moy crumble and rot to dust! Let what remains be scattered like ashes in the wind, and may I live to see the beginnings of this curse fulfilled!"

Then, screaming like a demon of the night, she turned and began running. Stumbling often, she picked herself up and ran aimlessly into the gathering darkness, deeper and deeper into the barren wilderness of Badenoch until she came at last upon an abandoned hut high on a wind-swept ledge. Venturing inside she discovered it was empty. Dropping to the floor, exhausted, she fell into a deep sleep.

When she awakened the next morning Fiona Urquhart found that overnight her hair had turned snow white. She never returned to her ancestral home, choosing instead to remain alone in her solitary isolation. Daily she went to visit the cairn, strewing it with colorful wild flowers and making certain that it was not disturbed. The rest of her time she occupied in aimless wanderings about the region, where at least once a day she faced toward the castle of Moy and repeated the words of the curse that she had pronounced.

Now many years had passed. Macintosh was long since dead, and having died without issue, a distant kinsman of the clan had inherited Moy, and along with it the curse. But Fiona Urquhart still lived, and as she finished the narrative of her terrible ordeal over a half-century earlier, there was for a moment absolute silence in the great hall of Moy. Then the old woman shifted her glance from young Macintosh and swept it across the faces of the assembled guests. "There will be no heir in this house," she cackled. "No heir, now or evermore!" And with those words she turned and strode from the hall.

The celebration and the banqueting were over,

for after this there could be no more song, no more merriment, and before long the guests had departed and the gloomy halls of Moy were all but deserted. And before another sun had set there was wailing and lamentation throughout the castle, for the infant had died, and the laird of Moy was again without an heir.

The Curse of
the Mummy's Foot

On a New Year's Eve not too many years ago a group of merrymakers were laughing, singing, dancing, and drinking as they awaited the first stroke of midnight heralding the new year. A large old grandfather clock that struck every hour with a series of deep, resonant bongs had been moved into the room for the occasion, and as the final hour of the old year gave way to the new one all the guests fell silent in anticipation. But before the last stroke, one guest, a rather mysterious man with the weatherbeaten look of a soldier of fortune, reached into the pocket of his dinner jacket and took out a small chamois pouch. His name was John Claudius and he said to no one in particular, "Who would like to have an unforgettable souvenir?"

"What is it?" someone asked.

"A mummy's foot," he replied casually, opening the pouch and drawing it out. Involuntary gasps escaped the lips of several present as they drew back in revulsion. Most of the guests, however, were drawn to it by morbid fascination, and though some shuddered as they did so, they did not shrink from taking it in their hands to examine it carefully.

It was tiny and shrunken, not much larger than the foot of a small child, and it was in a perfect state of preservation. At first glance it looked as if it had been skillfully fashioned out of brown leather by a master artist. The only thing that left no doubts in their minds was the unmistakable quality of its delicate and beautifully formed toenails. Claudius explained that he had recently returned from a trip to Egypt, and that the person who gave him the foot swore that it had once belonged to a dancer in the court of a pharoah six thousand years dead.

After it had been passed around several times, another guest, a young woman called Yvonne Day, who had seemed especially fascinated by the foot, said, "I'll take it. Who knows, maybe it will bring me good luck."

Claudis' face went grim for an instant, then he smiled and handed her the foot, saying, "Perhaps it might some day. But did it ever occur to you that it might bring you bad luck just as easily?"

"I'm not really worried about it," she replied, smiling. "I don't believe in those things anyway, but I think it's a fabulous curio, and it should make a marvelous conversation piece."

"You can be sure of it," said Claudius. "Consider it a New Year's present."

"Thank you, sir," she said, gaily. Then taking the foot she put it back into the chamois pouch and stuffed the pouch into her small evening bag.

Yvonne was spending the holiday with friends and was eager to show them her bizarre acquisition. The reaction of her hostess later that night was just about what she had expected.

"How ghastly!" the woman exclaimed, curling her upper lip in disgust. "Just do me a favor and put the horrid thing away where I can't see it. If I see it again, I think I'll get sick."

Yvonne could hardly keep from laughing at her hostess's reaction, but she had no intention of being rude. The moment she reached her room she put the mummy's foot back into the pouch and carefully placed it in the far corner of the dresser in the guest room she was occupying. It was nearly dawn and she was very tired from her evening of revelry. When she went to bed she fell asleep almost immediately.

She could not have been sleeping long because it was still dark. Yvonne found herself sitting up in bed, shivering, her heart pounding, her breath coming in short gasps. There was a mysterious cold and clammy feeling in the room — a weird presence that for no explainable reason seemed to fill her with terror. Pulling the covers up around her, she thought she heard a strange noise. Her heart began beating faster and she realized that she could hear distinctly an unfamiliar, slithery, rustling sound. Suddenly, with no advance warning, she felt a deathly coldness envelop her. Putting her hand to her mouth she gasped in terror. Then just as abruptly as it had appeared, the presence seemed to vanish and everything returned to normal. Heaving a deep, heavy sigh, she lay back and soon fell sound asleep again.

The next morning at breakfast Yvonne told her hostess about her frightening experience of the previous night. The woman shook her head and muttered, "I was afraid of something like this. It's that dreadful mummy's foot. You should never have accepted it."

"Don't be silly," replied Yvonne. "It was probably nothing more than my imagination. Besides, you know as well as I do, I overindulged at the party last night."

"That had nothing to do with it," insisted the hostess.

"Why do you say that?"

"Because the same thing happened to me last night too."

From that day on Yvonne was no longer so certain about the mummy's foot. For the next two weeks something disturbing and mysterious awakened her and her hostess every night shortly after midnight. Sometimes it felt like an icy breath on the face, other times it was the eerie slithery, rustling noise. But whatever it was, at the time it occurred the entire room would grow cold as a tomb, and whoever in the household was awakened would jump up with a start, in a cold sweat, heart pounding, and breath coming in short, jerky gasps.

At last it was more than Yvonne or anyone else in the house, for that matter, could take. "It has to be the mummy's foot," she said firmly one day. Taking it from the dresser drawer where she had put it when she first brought it home, she carefully tied the thong at the mouth of the pouch, placed it in a brown paper bag, and went outside determined to take it to the museum. As she was riding on the bus a disturbing thought en-

tered her mind. What if they refused to accept
it? What would she do then? She would certainly
not give it to anyone she knew, even someone she
didn't like. There was only one logical thing for
her to do. Carefully rolling up the paper bag
around its grisly contents, she surreptitiously
slid it under the seat, and hastily got off the bus
at the next stop.

That night when she went to bed she slept
soundly all night. No one else in the household
reported any further disturbances, and everyone
was thoroughly relieved. Nevertheless, Yvonne
was still curious about the mummy's foot and
she wondered where it was now, little dreaming
she would soon enough learn. At the moment,
however, she had other things to think about. She
was about to return home and had to concentrate
on myriad details such as packing, arranging for
her reservations, and seeing a few friends before
her departure.

Several months later Yvonne had to make an
unexpected trip back to the city on business and
she was invited to a dinner party by the friend
with whom she had stayed over the New Year's
holiday. Not only was the party at the same house
where she had met John Claudius, the man who
had given her the mummy's foot, he was again a
guest.

"I must say," she told him rather coolly, "You didn't exactly do me a favor when you gave me that mummy's foot. I didn't have a decent night's sleep from the moment I got it in the house."

He smiled mirthlessly and said, "I didn't guarantee it to be a lucky charm, you know."

"You didn't tell me that we would be frightened half out of our wits, either," she retorted.

"You seem to be in reasonably good health," he observed.

"No thanks to you and your awful mummy's foot. I'm just glad I got rid of it."

"Well," he said gravely, "I can't say that I really blame you. I hope it hasn't caused any problems for the one to whom you gave it."

"You didn't seem to show that kind of concern for me."

"I have a confession to make," he said. "I knew there was something strange about it at the time, but I didn't know the entire story. You see, I've just returned from another trip to Egypt, and now I know the whole truth. Promise me one thing though, when you hear what I have to say, tell the person who has it now."

"I'm afraid that's impossible," declared Yvonne. "I left it on a public bus. For all I know it could be in Timbuctoo by now."

"I hope it has been destroyed," he replied.

"Well for heaven's sake," exclaimed Yvonne. "Don't keep me in suspense. Tell me the story."

"To begin with," began Claudius, "I didn't tell you exactly how the foot came into my possession."

"I thought you bought it in a curio shop."

"No, I said nothing of the sort. I merely mentioned that someone gave it to me, and very vaguely at that. The truth of the matter is that I was paid quite handsomely to take it out of the country. Naturally I was curious, but the only thing that the man with whom I was dealing would say was that it was cursed and that he had to be rid of it within twenty-four hours. My first reaction was that it involved a bit of minor smuggling — I've never been a superstitious man. But the gentleman made it quite clear that he was only concerned with ridding himself of the thing. Accepting this as a minor eccentricity on the part of a wealthy man, I agreed to his terms, and took the foot out of the country."

"Weren't you at all suspicious?" asked Yvonne.

Claudius smiled. "I'm a confirmed cynic," he said. "And there are times when cynicism obliterates suspicion. I didn't believe the curse story, but I have seen many instances where the human mind turns fancy into reality. As I said, whatever

102

suspicions I entertained were purely material."

"But something happened to make you change your mind."

"Yes, it did. I have to explain that because I was doing a great deal of traveling, and felt I didn't need to maintain a large apartment, I had rented two rooms which suited me perfectly in the upper part of a private house. One evening, shortly after I brought the foot back from Egypt, my landlady came up. She was on the verge of tears. She said that she was worried about her young daughter; the child was either sick or losing her mind. When I asked her to explain she replied that the girl kept insisting that she saw a bare, dark brown foot peeping out from behind a curtain or scurrying about in closets. She was becoming so terrified that she had begun to lose her appetite, was afraid to go to sleep, and had grown terribly nervous.

"When she asked my advice I suggested that she bring the child to me. It occurred to me that she had heard her parents mention the mummy's foot. I had shown it to them and perhaps the thought of it had preyed on her mind and frightened her. So before they returned, I took the foot from its pouch and placed it on the mantelpiece. I felt that if she saw it there in the open she would realize that it was harmless. Unfortunately, no such thing happened. The very instant she spied the thing she began screaming. She had such a fit of hysterics her mother had to take her downstairs immediately."

"What happened after that?" asked Yvonne.

"Naturally I had a long talk with her parents later that evening. They swore that they had never mentioned the foot to the child. Yet there was no doubt about it. She recognized it the moment she set eyes on it. I was in a terribly awkward position. Although I wasn't especially attached to the foot I had every intention of keeping it. They made it very plain to me, however, that either I got rid of the foot or I would have to move. I had no choice. I had to return to Egypt on business a week later and I simply had no time to find other lodgings, so naturally I assured them that I would remove it from the house within twenty-four hours."

"What on earth made you bring it to the New Year's party?" Yvonne demanded.

Claudius smiled. "It's very simple. I couldn't bring myself to throw it in the garbage. It had been part of a living person once. I hoped that I would find someone who might want it, and I did. I found you."

"Well, now that you've found me again, I'd appreciate it if you'd tell me the whole story about that mummy's foot. I hate suspense."

"I can't say that I blame you," replied Claudius. "As I said, when I first agreed to take the foot out of Egypt I didn't believe the curse story at all. I thought about it after the incident involving my landlady's little girl. But after hearing your story, and learning what I did when I went back to Egypt, I'm not so skeptical any more. You see, the man who asked me to dispose of the foot in the first place did so because he was frightened. He admitted everything to me once he knew that it was gone. He had stolen the foot from an old tomb. It had been the foot of a favored dancer in the court of an ancient Egyptian king. She had become involved in a court intrigue for which she was sentenced to death. The intrigue, by the way, was a plot to assassinate the king, and the only person who knew the identity of the ringleader was the dancer. Furthermore, she died without ever having revealed his name. After her execution the king decreed that only her feet be mummified, because they had never offended him, so they were duly preserved, while the rest of her body was burned to ashes. The chief conspirator, who had survived because of the dancer's silence, was a high priest at the temple of Karnak. When he heard that the king was planning to keep the mummified feet in the royal house-

105

hold he wove a curse of great complexity about the feet."

"I don't quite understand," said Yvonne, frowning.

"You will," Claudius continued. "You see, he actually intended to put his curse on the king, but if he did it openly he faced the possibility of grave consequences, so in effect he cursed any person and any house that ever possessed the feet. Apparently it was quite a potent curse, because the king died soon afterwards. The dancer's feet were buried in his tomb along with all his other possessions."

"Was that the same tomb that your friend stole the foot from?" asked Yvonne.

"Oh, no," said Claudius. "You see, over the centuries grave robbers were quite active in Egypt. I have no idea, for example, of what ever happened to the other foot."

"Well frankly," declared Yvonne, "I'd just as soon not know, and that goes for the one you gave me too."

"I'm inclined to agree with you," Claudius said. "Who knows what may happen now that it's loose here in our own country."

Curses That Backfire

There is an old saying that "curses, like chickens, come home to roost." The following two short Chinese tales are perfect illustrations, and serve well as reminders that to seek revenge is not always necessarily the best course of action.

A man named Kao Ming Ching, who was in perfect health, got married, and though he was perfectly happy with his wife he began to suffer from a strange malady almost immediately after taking his new wife home. The moment he opened his eyes in the morning the room would swim and dizziness assailed him. Not only did he suffer from this inexplicable vertigo, he found himself short of breath and gasping as though he were about to choke.

At night when he fell exhausted into bed he began hearing terrifying cries like those of a small child being slowly strangled. One night after this had been going on for several months, Kao sat up and lit a lamp. To his astonishment he saw a tiny figure resembling a man no taller than one foot, dancing and jumping about over his bedclothes. As he made a move to reach out and seize it, the little creature disappeared. From then on, each night shortly after the cries began Kao would see the mysterious little figure, always running along the same path, and whenever he saw it the thing would vanish. Its presence was disturbing enough, but worse, as time passed Kao became weaker and weaker.

Recognizing that he was suffering from no ordinary illness, but was under some spell, Kao consulted a soothsayer. But the soothsayer's charms did nothing to alleviate Kao's distress.

One afternoon, before lying down for a nap, Kao hid a sword under his pillow. Then he took a basin of water and put it in the corner of the room at approximately the same spot where he saw the weird figure disappear each night. Having done these things Kao lay down and went to sleep. He had barely dozed off when he heard the familiar cries. Jumping up he saw his tiny tormentor, and seizing his sword he raised it threateningly. The creature fled, but before it could vanish it stumbled and fell splashing into the basin. Hastily Kao went over to the basin and looked inside. There floating face down was a small wooden man dressed in red with a bright red string tight about its neck. Retrieving the figure from the water and drying it off Kao burned it that day and from that moment on he was as healthy as he had been before getting married.

Later he learned that at the same time he burned the wooden man the village carpenter died, suddenly and mysteriously. Upon further investigation Kao discovered that the carpenter had constructed his bridal chamber. Disgruntled because Kao had refused to pay his original price, the carpenter hid a magical charm in the room with a curse intended to make Kao hang himself. When it failed to accomplish its original purpose and was burned, it brought destruction only to the man who had employed it.

* * *

An ancient Chinese chess master named Chao Ching Yao lived in the city of Hangchow. Chess was his entire life and the sound alone of chessmen moving across the board was enough to set his heart pounding with excitement. Whenever he saw others play he was impelled to stop and watch them, and as he was such an expert his presence was regarded as a high honor.

One day while passing by a certain temple he looked through the door and saw a Taoist priest playing chess with another man. Chao was unable to resist, so he turned, went inside, and watched the players at their game. To his disappointment the priest was not only a bad player, but a loud-mouth and a braggart. Finding it impossible to enjoy the match any further Chao turned his back and left the temple.

That night after attending to all the necessary business required of him that day Chao went to bed. He had barely extinguished his lamp when he saw two will-o-the-wisps darting about the room over his bed. They had barely flitted away when an evil spirit called a Kuei appeared. It had a fierce black face, glowing yellow eyes, and a gleaming row of jagged teeth. Glaring balefully at Chao, the Kuei raised a sword and snarled threateningly, but Chao defied the Kuei, showing no fear, and it disappeared from sight.

The next night shortly after retiring he was startled to hear a reedy little voice that seemed to be coming from his pillow. "What business is it of yours if I boast and play chess badly? It would not have hurt you to linger a while and watch. You have grievously insulted me. If you do not fear the sword let us see if you can resist my curse."

Recognizing the voice as the wandering soul of the Taoist, taking temporary leave of his body, Chao steeled himself for the worst. The voice began to utter an incantation. "Spirits of earth and heaven," it chanted, "take revenge for me, drive a spike into his heart!"

The thought of this made Chao shiver slightly, but he refused to let the angry soul get the better of him. Plugging his ears with wax, he relaxed and soon fell asleep. For one full month the incantations continued, calling upon the spirits to destroy Chao, but nothing happened. Then unexpectedly one night the soul of the Taoist appeared to Chao, bowed respectfully, and said, "I have been troubling you partly out of anger and partly in hopes of extorting silver from you, but you have not been frightened and you have not been harmed. Since the incantations of the sorcerer have failed, my curse has fallen upon my own head. Yesterday I took leave of this life. I must make restitution for the ill I have done you, therefore my soul is at your disposal."

Fearing a trick of some sort Chao did not answer, but the next day he went to the temple and inquired after the chess-playing Taoist. The man had slit his throat the day before, but from that time on his soul remained at Chao's service and warned him a day in advance of whatever was going to happen — his penance for uttering a curse that was undeserved.